CU00796234

MOZART · SONATAS FOR PIANOFORTE · VC

MOZART

Sonatas for Pianoforte

Volume I

Edited by
STANLEY SADIE

Fingering and performance notes by
DENIS MATTHEWS

THE ASSOCIATED BOARD OF
THE ROYAL SCHOOLS OF MUSIC

THEMATIC INDEX

VOLUME I

Sonata in C

K279/189*d*

Allegro

Page 12

Sonata in F

K280/189*e*

Allegro assai

26

Sonata in B flat

K281/189*f*

Allegro

40

Sonata in E flat

K282/189*g*

Adagio

58

Sonata in G

K283/189*h*

Allegro

68

Sonata in D

K284/205*b*

Allegro

84

Sonata in C

K309/284*b*

Allegro con spirito

114

Sonata in A minor

K310/300*d*

Allegro maestoso

136

Sonata in D

K311/284*c*

Allegro con spirito

158

VOLUME II

Sonata in C

K330/300*h*

Allegro moderato

Page 12

Sonata in A

K331/300*i*

Andante grazioso

28

Sonata in F

K332/300*k*

Allegro

48

Sonata in B flat

K333/315*c*

Allegro

72

Fantasy in C minor

K475

Adagio

95

Sonata in C minor

K457

Molto allegro

105

Sonata in F

K533

Allegro

126

Sonata in C

K545

Allegro

148

Sonata in B flat

K570

Allegro

162

Sonata in D

K576

Allegro

176

INTRODUCTION

A new edition of an established series of classics will, it is hoped, stimulate some reassessment of the works themselves. It may be argued that Mozart of all composers is in no need of such reappraisal. Yet there has long been a tendency to underestimate his piano sonatas, partly through their over-familiarity as 'teaching pieces'. Maybe that taken as a whole they are far less important in Mozart's output than his piano concertos, but how or why should the sonatas be blamed? The concerto in its nature was public music, in which the rivalry of solo and orchestra proved a constant challenge to Mozart's operatic genius. It is no accident that twelve of his greatest concertos were written expressly for his concerts in Vienna in the years 1784–6, during which time he produced only one piano sonata, the C minor. The fact that this Sonata, along with its accompanying Fantasy, is the most dramatic of all the solo works points to the fruitful effect of cross-influences, which should always be borne in mind by the performer. Parallels in character and texture are sometimes suggested in the 'performing notes' of this edition but are offered mainly as guide-lines to encourage the player's own initiative.

The examination question that amusingly invited an essay 'in defence of the Mozart piano sonatas' offered plenty of scope. It could be observed that, despite the grandeur and pathos of such works as the A minor and C minor, the sonata was in general a more modest and domestic form for Mozart, most likely to be written down for the use of others, or to execute a commission, or with a view to publication. Why else should he spend time over a work he could carry in his astonishing memory or improvise? From Augsburg in 1777 he wrote that he had played 'all of a sudden a magnificent sonata in C major'. He had no immediate need to capture it on paper; but only a few days later we find him 'composing' a work in this key for Rosa Cannabich, the young daughter of the Mannheim composer. Although it would be quite misleading to dismiss the more light-weight of Mozart's sonatas as 'didactic' or 'utility' music, this is not to deny their great educational value. Mozart himself described his C major Sonata, K545, as 'for beginners', but in this respect it is worth recalling Artur Schnabel's remark that 'children are given Mozart because of the quantity of the notes; grown-ups avoid him because of the *quality* of the notes, which to be sure, is elusive'.

Schnabel's witty paradox was not intended to inhibit either young or old in their approach to music that, to quote him again, 'is better than it can be played'. The quest for the elusive provides the eternal challenge, the reward – and the discontent – for serious artists of any age. Mozart in fact referred to his first six piano sonatas as 'those difficult works'. He played them repeatedly on his tours and wrote excitedly of the effect of the D major, K284, on Stein's fortepianos at Augsburg, enough to refute the notion that such 'early' Mozart should really be played on the harpsichord. A knowledge of Mozart's letters and of the chronology of his works is an important step towards stylistic interpretation.

Chronology

The piano sonatas cover about fifteen years of Mozart's life but fall into at least five 'periods'. The first six, K279–284, come rather earlier than the original Köchel numbers implied (hence the revised K numbers given in modern editions): they date from early 1775 and their key-scheme suggests intention as a set, despite the separate commission of K284 from Baron von Dürnitz of Munich. The next three, K309–311, were written on Mozart's travels to Mannheim and Paris in 1777–8, and of these the A minor, K310, stands apart as a prophetic masterpiece. The following four, K330–3, used also to be dated from the Paris visit, but recent research places them four or five years later, well into Mozart's mature Vienna period. It is generally agreed that the C minor, K457, comes from 1784, which also produced the six concertos from K449 to K459; and its related Fantasy, K475, from the following year. The remaining four, including the purposely 'easy' K545 in C, were composed in 1788–9. The spare textures of K570 in B♭ and the severer contrapuntal hurdles of K576 in D are tests of a player's control and sense of style. Counterpoint also plays a great part in the opening movements of K533 in F, to which Mozart added an extended version of the Rondo, K494.

Two further 'sonatas' were included in the earlier Associated Board edition. The B♭, K498a, is a four-movement work of doubtful origin, incorporating a mutilated version of the variations from the B♭ Concerto, K450, and a widely modulating rondo based on memories of more than one of Mozart's six-eight concerto-finales. The F major, K547a, derives from the Violin and Piano Sonata, K547, and the finale of K545, showing more signs of Mozart's own hand. There seems little justification, however, for including either in the series of authentic sonatas.

Instruments

The absolute purist seeking to recapture the precise sounds of Mozart's day has a difficult if not impossible task. This is not to belittle the enthusiastic revivers of earlier instruments or the responsibility of the modern pianist in knowing about them. It is a far cry from the light touch and silvery tone of a wooden-framed fortepiano to the felt-covered hammers and iron frame familiar from the mid-nineteenth century onwards. Whether Mozart would have approved of the sound of a modern concert grand is open to doubt, but it is certain that he never envisaged his sonatas being played in a large hall to audiences of thousands. Yet to insist on confining him to an eighteenth-century fortepiano would hardly do justice to a composer who was above all a practical musician and whose music has such a universal appeal and relevance. In the long run it is surely the manner of playing that takes precedence over the exact timbre of an instrument, bearing in mind that the timbre was a variable factor even in Mozart's lifetime. He welcomed the latest developments of the fortepiano and, like Bach, was not averse to transcribing a work from one medium to a very different one. He arranged his two-piano Fugue in C minor for strings, and his C minor Wind Serenade for string quintet. This prerogative cannot be taken as a precedent for the tamperings of others, but it indicates that tone-character was to some degree secondary to musical thought.

If we accept that the Mozart sonatas will be played most often on some variety of modern piano as the 'clavier' of our day, this should not dull the performer's ear into complacency over texture, sonority, dynamics and phrasing. It is neither desirable nor practical to imitate the fortepiano, but it is essential to emulate its clarity and to guard against extremes of dynamics or thickness of texture, especially in the lower registers. There are no places in Mozart calling for the Beethovenish injunction that 'the piano must break!', but there is the opposite danger of underplaying the drama so inherent in much of Mozart's music. In the first movement of the A minor Sonata, K310, he indicated abrupt contrasts of *ff* and *pp*, but even in the gentler world of the F major, K332, the first move into D minor is like a step from comedy into tragedy. In neither case is the sonority that of Beethoven's 'Appassionata', but the lighter and more transparent texture does not preclude a similar intensity of feeling. Here and elsewhere such operatic parallels as the opening scene of *Don Giovanni* or the finale to Act 2 of *Figaro* are the closest guides to the music's character.

Interpretation

Such parallels – opera, the concerto, the symphony, chamber music – can only strengthen interpretation. Conjectures about Mozart's own playing are helped by two well-known remarks from his letters: his insistence that passage-work should flow 'like oil', and his claim that he always played 'in strict time'. Even in *tempo rubato* he maintained that freedom in the melodic line should not disturb the basic pulse in the left hand, though his abhorrence of expressionless rigidity was equally clear, summed up in his opinion of Clementi as 'a mere *mechanicus*'. Reports vary from praise of Mozart's singing tone to Beethoven's reservation about his harpsichord-like treatment of the piano, though this was recalled years after their one meeting in 1787. It is more to the point to note that Mozart continued to own a clavichord in his later years. As far as the piano is concerned the recurring advice to *practise* without pedal does not mean to play without pedal. Mozart was well aware of the importance of the damper-pedal – or its forerunner, the knee-lever. Caution over pedalling should, however, be governed by musical sense as well as sonority. Even when the harmony does not object, good sense may do so: the upbeat into the Andante of the A minor Sonata, K310, will lose its melodic quality as a single voice if pedalled

through, and so will the cadence-figure in the first movement of the D major, K576.

Mozart's ability to turn limitations into assets is illustrated by his treatment of the shorter five-octave compass of the fortepiano. Far from being a hindrance to him, the upper limit of F above the treble stave (f''') was a stimulus to invention, causing him to re-think and often to enhance passages when they returned at a higher pitch. An obvious example comes in the first movement of the Bb Sonata, K333, where the phrase from b.46 is extended from five to eleven bars when it returns at b.142, an inspired change brought about solely through the limitation. To carry similar passages beyond Mozart's original compass, as some editors and players have done, not only distorts his line of thought: it produces anachronisms and may even remove the cause of a masterstroke.

The Urtext

The time is mostly past when editors 'interpreted' the text without acknowledgement, adding or changing dynamics, dots, accents and phrase-marks at random, extending passages beyond their compass, writing out ornaments in full, and so forth. The earlier Associated Board edition of the Mozart sonatas suffered in just this way, having been based on a heavily-edited and now discredited German text. Attitudes and responsibilities have changed radically in the last half-century. We live in an Urtext age and with good reason. By 'Urtext' we imply an edition that aims to preserve the original text, separating necessary editorial marks, queries and comments by the use of brackets or different type. Dr Sadie's own introductions will testify to our joint concern for authenticity and precision, and to the problems encountered in determining exactly what the composer's intentions may be.

The scope and purpose of a teaching edition, such as the present one, go further, of course; but the addition of fingering and the realization of ornaments above the main text are for the guidance of students and neither obligatory nor, it is insisted, at variance with the spirit of the Urtext. It was felt cumbersome and undesirable to incorporate pedal-marks, since the subtle and much-abused art of pedalling depends so much on the player's own ear for sonority, harmony and musical sense. Mozart left no original fingerings or pedal marks, though reference to both may be found along with other interpretative suggestions in my performing notes.

Denis Matthews
Newcastle upon Tyne, 1980

EDITORIAL PREFACE

The objective in the editing of these works has been the obvious one: the production of a clear text that accurately represents Mozart's intentions. That is not always easy. Not all Mozart's autographs survive; when they do, their texts are not free of ambiguities, internal contradictions, or errors, and they may conflict with contemporary printed texts that show definite signs of bearing Mozart's authority. There is no simple or uniform solution. Sometimes a choice must be offered to the performer, occasionally by means of an alternative text, more often through a footnote drawing attention to a different possible reading (which is likely to be discussed more fully in the Textual Notes preceding the sonata concerned).

Along the principles traditional to literary textual criticism, but less common in its musical counterpart, only those sources that have clear authority have been consulted; there is little to be gained in calling upon the opinions of secondary editors or publishers of the late 18th century or the 19th, whose versions represent nothing more than their own subjective interpretations of earlier sources (little use, for example, has been made of the several early editions that are clearly copied from first editions, or of the heavily edited text of the sonatas in the 1799 Breitkopf & Härtel *Oeuvres complettes* which represents the first editions of a number of sonatas). The general principle has been to use the autograph, where it survives, and any edition of Mozart's lifetime that may bear his authority, but nothing beyond. In the absence of the autograph, recourse has been made to other authoritative sources, for example the copy of K309/284*b* by Leopold Mozart or the dedication copy of K457 that Mozart signed. Only occasionally, in the absence of both an autograph and an authoritative contemporary edition, a more distant source has perforce been used. Full details of the sources are given in the prefatory material to each sonata.

In the printing of the text a distinction has been made between original and editorial markings. Slurs and ties added editorially are indicated by a small perpendicular stroke; editorial staccato marks (whether dots or wedges), dynamic markings and accidentals are indicated by the use of smaller type. Such added articulation and dynamic marks are not of course detailed in the Textual Notes (unless there is special reason to do so); usually they are justified by analogy with parallel passages. Where they are not added but an analogy seems to exist, it is usually because there is some pattern – which we should presume to be intentional – behind their omission in the source. Doubtful cases are detailed in the Textual Notes.

There are certain features of Mozart's notation, or to some extent of late 18th-century notation generally, that seem to be idiosyncratic or pointless or simply old-fashioned, like the use of double stems in chords or the provision of separate dynamic markings for the two hands. These have mostly been retained. It is not always practical to follow Mozart's sometimes hastily written autograph precisely over double stemming, and often he is, it seems, pointlessly inconsistent; but this practice in general is worth following as sometimes it may clarify the part-writing and usefully show how Mozart, when composing the music, envisaged it. Separate dynamic mark-

ings for the hands, equally, represent Mozart's own view of their independence, and their retention often elucidates the phrase structure.

Mozart's use of different kinds of staccato mark has been much discussed, and some scholars have suggested that his differentiation is neither consistent nor meaningful. It is true that it is not consistent, in that he sometimes uses different kinds of mark in a passage that occurs more than once. Yet certain patterns are regular and discernible. Repeated short, light staccato notes are nearly always given dots, and notes demanding accentuation or standing at the end of a phrase more often carry wedges (or dashes). Sometimes the wedge sign, in fact, represents an accent rather than a staccato (as on those occasions, rare ones, when it appears over a long note). An attempt has been made here to retain Mozart's differentiation as precisely as possible, though his numerous gradations between dot and wedge even in a single passage often make this impossible. In sonatas where the principal source is printed, the usage in the original text is preferred; it is clear from comparisons between autograph texts and printed ones, in the sonatas where we have both, that engravers made little attempt to differentiate and favoured either a consistent dot or a consistent wedge. But wherever an autograph has clear differentiation, we follow it.

Mozart's use of slurs represents another problematic area. Sometimes he was meticulous; but often he added slurs with only a generalized intention of asking for legato playing – many times, for example, an 'Alberti-type' passage in the left hand will at one point be slurred four notes at a time, at another eight, and at another not at all. Often when he moved from one system to the next he broke the pattern; and of course there are divergences between passages that appear more than once. Even some quite critical melodic passages show such variation. Where it seems to be significant, it has been retained; if Mozart will not make up his mind, it would be impertinent to do so on his behalf. But where any significance seems remote, or the variation is clearly the result of careless or hasty markings, the passage is uniformly notated and the original readings of altered passages are itemized in the Textual Notes. Sometimes – another procedure akin to those of literary criticism – it has been thought best to follow a more complex reading where there is a choice between that and a simpler one, since the former is less likely to have been written carelessly or accidentally.

Mozart was often very sparing of dynamic markings. The absence of a marking at the beginning of a movement of course implies *forte*, and that has been supplied as necessary (in small type), except in certain movements entirely devoid of dynamic markings. Other dynamic markings that are clearly implied, normally by analogy, are added similarly, and in a few problematic passages where Mozart's indications seem inconsistent or untenable a possible solution is put forward. It seems clear that Mozart, in preparing a sonata for publication, added – or at least consented to the addition of – dynamic markings, and such markings from the printed texts are included without differentiation (though their source is mentioned, in each case, in the Textual Notes).

Some aspects of the original notation have been modernized without mention. For example, Mozart's *forte, for:* and *f:* are given as *f*, his *piano, pia:* and *p:* as *p*. The usage of accidentals is modernized, though added ones are reckoned as editorial. Grace-notes are given as modern semiquavers (rarely demisemiquavers), not in Mozart's form – a crossed-through quaver (meaning in fact a semiquaver, not an acciaccatura).

Editorial realizations of ornaments are shown in small notes above the text at the first occurrence of the ornament concerned in each movement. These realizations are based on the leading sources contemporary with Mozart, such as C. P. E. Bach's *Versuch über die wahre Art das Clavier zu spielen* (1753–62), Leopold Mozart's *Versuch einer gründlichen Violinschule* (1756) and Daniel Gottlob Türk's *Clavierschule* (1789). Our suggestions should not be taken as mandatory; any proper realization must take account of the tempo chosen for the movement concerned and the player's capabilities, and in a trill a player should feel free to play more notes, or fewer, as seems right. No ornament that feels awkward to the player, or sounds clumsy, is being satisfactorily realized. A player who wants to vary the realization of ornaments more extensively, however, would be well advised first to consult the writings of contemporary authorities, or failing that a summary of their views in a good modern reference work; he should note that except in very rare circumstances a trill should begin on the upper note in music of this period.

I should like, finally, to record my thanks to the librarians and others who have made available to me films or photocopies of Mozart autographs, other manuscripts or early editions in their custody. Details of these are given in the note on sources in the Textual Notes preceding each sonata. Dr Alan Tyson merits particular thanks for generously lending me copies from his collection of two important early publications, one of them being the extremely rare first printing of three sonatas (K330/300*h*, 331/300*i* and 332/300*k*), showing some important divergences from familiar texts that, as far as I am aware, have hitherto been unknown to editors of these works. I should also refer to the single largest collection of autographs, that formerly in the Preussische Staatsbibliothek, Berlin, and now in the Biblioteka Jagiellońska, Kraków (but not now available for inspection, or for filming); films of these, made before the 1939–45 war and regrettably unclear in certain details, are held in the Photogramm-Archiv of the Österreichische Nationalbibliothek, Vienna, and I have kindly been supplied with copies of these by the authorities of that library and of the Bayerische Staatsbibliothek, Munich, to whom I am grateful.

STANLEY SADIE
London, 1981

Abbreviations in Textual Notes

cf. – *confer* [compare]; dsq – demisemiquaver; edn – edition; K – no. in Köchel catalogue of Mozart's works (no. before / is original no., no. after is that in 6th edn, 1964); lh – left hand; movt – movement; q – quaver; rh – right hand; sq – semiquaver; stacc. – staccato

Pitch – *c'* is middle C, *d'* the note above, *b* the note below; *c"* and *c'''* one and two octaves above, *c*, *C* and *C'* one, two and three octaves below

Numerals – arabic numerals in roman normally denote bar nos.; arabic in italic denote note nos. within the bar, counting left to right, chords downwards, and including all grace notes as notated

SONATA in C, K279/189d

Apart from four unpublished and presumably lost keyboard sonatas dating from about 1766, this C major Sonata of 1775 is Mozart's first. By that time he had already produced about thirty symphonies, of which at least two – K183 in G minor and K201 in A major – have become firm repertory works. In this light it is easy to undervalue the first piano sonatas which are in their nature more intimate and less sensational. Like the lost earlier ones they were useful to Mozart on his travels, and the travels themselves brought many influences to bear on his natural style. His unique gift was the ability to assimilate such things and to make them his own. The imprint of Haydn may be detected in the finale of K279, and in fact six Haydn sonatas, Hob.xvi/21–26, had been published in 1774. J. C. Bach and Michael Haydn have also been mentioned for their influences on the young Mozart, but the player will do well to look beyond the common features and clichés that abound in early music for the fortepiano. The Alberti-type bass was one such device, and to render it casually or clumsily will simply distract from the more characterful offerings of the r.h. – as in bb.5–8 of the first movement and the opening of the slow movement of the present work. Note that all three movements are in sonata form with purposeful developments depending on the performer's key-sense. Recapitulations are also adventurous, bringing a changed order of events in the first two movements and an unexpected bonus in the finale.

1 The chords in the opening theme should be only slightly spread, throwing the emphasis on to the upper melodic notes. Notice that the l.h. figure returns later (bb.12, 20, 33) and keep the semitone clear of pedal. The trill in b.2 is also a recurring feature, e.g. bb.14–15, but should not upset the semiquaver flow: an upper mordent or even a crushed grace-note will suffice to give the necessary bite. In b.5 the r.h. phrase begins *after* the first quaver, thus throwing b.8 into relief. This section is best taken more lightly, with the contrast in touch between b.9 and b.11 carefully shown, allowing the chords in b.12–13 to make their harmonic point more sonorously. The B♮s are a surprise, but Mozart compensated by striking out to the sharp side of the dominant key in b.17, a gesture that can be made with brilliant resolution. The dynamic changes in b.28–30 (and again in b.37) are capricious. Consider b.29 as a development and diminution of the grace-note idea and enjoy its amusing reshaping in b.90. The repeated notes in b.31 need articulating clearly: other fingering possibilities are *345* or *5* throughout.

2 The notation presents a problem, since Mozart establishes a l.h. triplet rhythm that affects the whole movement, including the r.h. melodic line from b.3 onwards. Flexible and even casual notating of twos and fours in a context of threes (and the use of variable dotted notes) was common Baroque practice and survived in Schubert, Brahms and even Debussy, where a single note-head with two stems might bring the second of a duplet and the third of a triplet together. The lead-back in b.42 hints at a certain freedom of expression and the ornaments in b.1

should bear this in mind. It would seem natural to treat upbeat quavers (end of b.2 etc) as triplets since they lead to triplets, and to make semiquaver upbeats noticeably shorter. It is suggested that the l.h. in bb. 15–16 should adjust itself to the r.h. triplets also. The r.h. in b.21 presumably matches the figure of the following bars. Whatever decisions are taken, the aim throughout is to achieve a flowing tempo with a *cantabile* line sustained in spite of the many changes of register. Therefore the contrasts of *f* and *p* should be tempered expressively with special care over the 'vocal' leaps in bb.3–4 and bb.14–15.

3 Deliver the opening minims firmly and evenly and note that four bars of *p* are answered by a six-bar *f* phrase. The l.h. legato figure requires careful shading with precise rests since it forms a slender link with the second group (b.24). Accompanying quavers from b.3 are lightly separated. A lively two-in-a-bar (say ♩ =120) should take account of the varied r.h. slurs in bb.11–18, which call for a flute-like agility. In bb.34–36 the three bars may be taken in a continuing legato. The 'bonus' (bb.132–146) is a surprise re-visit of the main second-group theme. Refer back in thought to its r.h.–l.h. exchanges in the development (bb.57–68) and 'score' it with a Haydnish alternation of woodwind and tutti. NB: the grace-note in b.87 is thematic and best approached with the fingering suggested.

D.M.

TEXTUAL NOTES

Composition   Munich, Jan–Feb 1775

Sources   1st movement, André edition (Offenbach, *c* 1841)
(autograph lost; the André firm is known to have
had access to Mozart's autographs, and comparison
between the surviving autograph of the second and
third movements and André's text indicates that he
followed it closely). 2nd and 3rd movements:
autograph (formerly in Preussische Staatsbibliothek,
Berlin)

Notes

1st movt
bar

60   RH, arpeggio sign missing

2nd movt
bar

20   LH and RH each have superfluous *p* (start of new
          system)

3rd movt
bar

99   RH, last 4 notes slurred in pairs
100   RH, last 4 notes slurred together

SONATA in C

K279/189d (1775)

Allegro

© 1979 by The Associated Board of the Royal Schools of Music

A.B. 1689

18

Allegro

SONATA in F, K280/189e

The amended Köchel numbers of Mozart's first six keyboard sonatas place them earlier than was once suspected. Yet he obviously set store by them, repeatedly referred to them as 'difficult', and at all events found them useful on his travels to Augsburg, Mannheim and Paris in 1777–8. In Augsburg he certainly tried them out on Stein's forte-pianos, which he much admired. Without underplaying the wit and drama of the outer movements of this F major Sonata, or the tender but intense pathos of its Adagio, the sensitive player will bear in mind that the wooden-framed instrument of Mozart's day produced a lighter and more silvery and transparent sound than its modern descendant, whether concert grand or modest upright. Such awareness of style also demands the utmost discretion over pedalling, far too subtle and personal a matter to risk incorporating suggestions in this edition along with other editorial marks (fingering, ornaments). Here too the ear must be the judge, accepting nothing that blurs harmonic or musical sense.

1   The opening theme is a case in point, since the l.h. crotchet steps require a fraction of air between them to match the physical needs of the r.h. repeated chords (though the dotted crotchet in b.2 should be fully held). As to tempo, *assai* surely refers to character rather than speed, the main task being to negotiate both triplets and semiquavers within a basic pulse. The crotchet movement holds this all together: therefore take care to match b.27 with b.1. In general the *f* and *p* contrasts should be taken *subito* without going to Beethovenish extremes. Nevertheless the long triplet passage from b.13 may find an interpretative guide in the melodic triplets of the 'Waldstein' first movement – second subject continuation – and here the l.h. rests are vital in view of the 'false relations' that ensue in b.18, etc. Check the speed of the new semiquaver figure in b.28 against the previous triplets to ensure a smooth resumption in b.35. Note that from here the *f* bars are evenly accented (do not be misled into an exaggerated *staccato*), the *p* bars smooth. For this reason the l.h. at the start of the development, b.57, may be preferred *legato*. Whether context and notational conventions permit the r.h. answers (b.58 etc.) to adopt the lazier triplet rhythm is debatable. Better not, since they are soon explained as a variant of the semiquaver figure that returns in b.68. Whereas the thirds in bb.75–77 may be felt more satisfying musically when divided between the hands there is no doubt that the upper voice in bb.101 and 103 should be taken over by the l.h. to leave the r.h. free to continue the triplets. The lead-back in bb.81–82 is subtly abrupt, needing careful handling with no suspicion of a *crescendo*.

2   Many have pointed out this movement's likeness to the slow movement of Haydn's F major Sonata, Hob.XVI/23, of the same time. Both turn to a siciliano rhythm in the tonic minor. Mozart's opening figure is imitated contrapuntally in the following bars, an excuse for starting its trill on the main note in place of the customary upper one (both realizations are suggested in the text). The dynamics are often related to expressive harmonic moves, e.g. bb.4, 13, 15. This point is further intensified by the minor-key recapitulation of the second group from b.43, wonderfully enhanced and extended. The chromaticism of bb.55–56 and the reshaping of the cadence figure should be compared with earlier parallel places. The gravity of this movement may be likened to that of the much-later Adagio of the A major Concerto, K488, also in a siciliano-like six-eight. Some editions changed this to *andante,* presumably to warn against the danger of dragging. Though misguided and presumptuous, the danger should be noted in the present movement also.

3   The finale thrives on lightness of texture, thus throwing into relief the mock-fiery outbursts in the development. The precise repeated Fs in the first full bar should be in mind when the dotted rhythm intervenes in b.38. Changes of finger are recommended to ease such repetition but are not obligatory for a player with a good finger-touch and a light arm. The printed suggestions have many possible variants. There is humour in the pauses that precede this theme. Among other details note the sudden *p* in bb.2–4 and regard bb.98–101 as a reference to bb.25–28 with attention to the l.h. notation in each case.

D.M.

TEXTUAL NOTES

Composition   Munich, Jan–Feb 1775

Source   autograph (formerly in Preussische Staatsbibliothek, Berlin)

Notes

1st movt
bar
64   possibly tie between 1st 2 notes, RH

3rd movt
bar
115   slur over whole bar; but cf. 8

SONATA in F

Allegro assai

K280/189*e* (1775)

© 1978 by The Associated Board of the Royal Schools of Music

A.B. 1676

Adagio

Presto

SONATA in B flat, K281/189*f*

1 A *forte* opening is implied, both by the *piano* in b.5 and the parallel dynamics in the recapitulation (b.70). The juxaposition of triplets and demisemiquavers characterizes the first subject and its development, and will present no problem to the player who masters the rhythmic swing of b.7. For this reason the demisemiquavers of b.1 need careful articulation: it is advisable to separate them from the trill. Although a case can be made for beginning on the main note (see b.70, where the C has already been taken in the upbeat) the upper note adds spice, and lines up with the dissonant B♭s and Cs of the next two crotchet beats. Despite variety in surface detail, the first four bars make a single sentence, rising by steps to the G of b.3 and falling away again: the quaver chords in b.4 reflect those in b.3 and demand a slight separation. Hence a short appoggiatura is recommended. Avoid a fussy echo effect in bb.10–12; it will spoil Mozart's own in b.13. The whole of the transition has the quality of brilliant string writing, with a lively cello part from b.12 onwards, matching the r.h. meticulously at the cadence in b.16–17. There is no need to change fingers on the repeated notes (bb.17 and 19) though players who wish to do so have ample time and choice. The passage-work in bb.22–27 gives a clue to the tempo, a steady two in which demisemiquavers may still be melodic without making the triplets of the first subject stick. Six notes will suffice for the trill-plus-turn in bb.23 and 25, and a final turn will help to clinch the cadence at b.33. A *forte* at b.38 is missing, but again implied (see b.107).

Although the opening of the development derives from b.27, play it with the enthusiasm of a new discovery. No pedal should cloud the dissonances hidden in the l.h. figure, especially in bb.43–44, and no *diminuendo* should spoil the change of colour at b.45. The lower register enables Mozart to expand the triplets in b.47, a feature that should be relished for the virtuoso viola-violin duet it sets off. Remember that G minor was a tragic key for Mozart (b.55) and E♭ was a warmly sonorous one (b.63), and do not withhold a natural feeling of *crescendo* into b.70 but save it for the last half-bar. The recapitulation goes its different way through the simple device of taking the note F as the existing dominant instead of a new tonic (b.86), but the various changes of octave are by no means predictable (e.g. bb.94, 103, 106) and have subtle emotional significance.

2 Imagine the opening octave as a well-timed continuo chord with overtones felt if not heard, and the descending thirds as clarinets. The epithet 'amoroso' points to a special mood, tender rather than passionate, and the original marks *crescendo* and *decrescendo* make their first appearance in the sonatas: they should be carefully judged, leading to and away from the dominant chord in b.4. Note too how tenderly Mozart approaches the dominant key, *piano* after *forte* (b.19 onwards), clinching the modulation with a cross-rhythm (hemiola) reflected in the l.h. accompaniment (bb.24–25). Short grace-notes here will link up with those in bb.17 and 19. The reshaping of bb.12–13 in bb.43–44 should also be felt and appreciated, thus binding the exposition together. The miniature development turns out to be a simple dominant prepara-

tion for the return, but the minor inflections are a surprise, both the G♭ in b.53 and the l.h. C♭ in b.54. So are the triplet variants from b.59, and the unforeseen new route taken by the transition theme.

3 B♭ was one of Mozart's favourite concerto keys, and the finale of the early K238 also breaks easily from a gavotte-like theme into triplet figuration. The *piano* and *forte* (see the finale of K333, another B♭ sonata) yield a natural contrast when thought of as solo and tutti, and the short cadenza at b.43 and the trills at b.114 reinforce the parallel. In bb.8–10 the triplets are best thought of as groups of three in which the bass is held for harmonic reasons: no single instrument will play the r.h. part successfully alone, or match the continuation. The second subject theme (b.28) should not be rhythmically influenced by the triplet accompaniment, and the upper-note trills in bb.39–42 (also b.136) should not take the *fp* away from the main note. The character and key scheme of the middle episodes, first G minor (b.52) and then E♭ (b.90) may profitably be compared with similar changes of mood in the first movement development. Needless to say, the timing of the return in b.71 must be exact: apart from the rhythmic placing of the 'gavotte' upbeat it takes a full bar-and-a-half for the shock of the spread chord to register itself as the dominant seventh of the home-key. The long trills from bb.114 and 119 need no final E♮ to complete them: it is supplied in the theme itself. The *forte* at the very end is *subito,* and the crotchets of this figure demand the slight separation instinctive to wind and string players, which pianists will do well to emulate.

D.M.

TEXTUAL NOTES

Composition Munich, Jan–Feb 1775

Source autograph (formerly in Preussische Staatsbibliothek, Berlin)

Notes

2nd movt original tempo 'Andantino amoroso', changed by Mozart

bar

68 original slurring as 10, and no tie to 1st note of next bar; Mozart seems to have struck out the slur with stacc. wedges. The variant is uncharacteristic; possibly Mozart intended to change the articulation in 10 too.

3rd movt

bar

27 LH 2nd crochet $b'\natural$

30 ornament sign ambiguous; this seems likeliest reading (also 126)

77–8,
148–9 RH slurring as shown; cf. 6–7, 49–50

SONATA in B flat

K281/189f (1775)

* Bars 1, 5, 70, 74: an alternative notation of the trill is suggested

Nor can its interpretation as a simple turn be ruled out.

© Copyright 1970 by The Associated Board of the Royal Schools of Music

A. B. 1514

Andante amoroso

RONDEAU
Allegro

55

A. B. 1514

SONATA in E flat, K282/189g

1 This is the only Mozart piano sonata to begin with a slow movement, unless we include the Andante variations of K331 or play the Fantasy, K475, as a prelude to the C minor Sonata, K457. The broad tempo is more easily captured by thinking in advance of the demisemiquaver lead-back in b.15. The form is unusual in that the impressive opening phrase is by-passed until the coda, where it is wonderfully reshaped, and the brief reference to it in b.16 makes its point in three ways: a sudden *piano*, a harmonic shock, and a diminution of the opening figure. The effect of all this is stronger when the repeats are made. In character the movement has much in common with the slow movements of the violin concertos of the following year (1775) and the theme in bb.11–12 will be better played by a pianist who has heard a good violinist play the D major, K218. The slurs here and in the recapitulation (b.29) are ambiguous in the autograph, but the demisemiquaver figure leading into b.12 shows its derivation more clearly when phrased in twos and *not* joined to the previous semiquaver. *Cantabile* should be cultivated throughout, and the frequent *p* and *f* alternations are expressive rather than dramatic, leading as they often do from the l.h. at the half-bar (b.4 and elsewhere). Mozart's enthusiastic approval of Stein's fortepianos in Augsburg should be remembered, and so should the remark in a letter to his father (October 23, 1777): 'Everyone is amazed that I can always keep strict time. What these people cannot grasp is that in tempo rubato in an Adagio, the left hand should go on playing in strict time. With them the left hand always follows suit.' Playing in strict time will nevertheless allow every semiquaver in b.8 and b.26 to carry the weight of a new harmony, and the pathos of the minor key should contrast with the prevailing serenity. The r.h. rests in b.4 are part of the theme's character: only a touch of pedal on each beat is permissible.

2 The tempo is like that of the minuet from Beethoven's Op.49 no.2 Sonata, though Mozart's phrase-lengths are infinitely more capricious: four bars answered by six, with a two-bar codetta expanded into four at the end of the first minuet. After the first repeat the *forte* chords need only slight spreading (and slight separation) and the upper chromatic descent must be brought out clearly. In bb.18–22 the r.h. must balance meticulously, matching the l.h. of the opening. Throughout both minuets the dotted rhythm is sharp, contrasting well with the lazier triplets in the passage-work of the second (b.37, etc.).

3 The finale demands the precision and character of good string-quartet playing, and a casual l.h. will ruin its effect. At the start the accompaniment echoes the pointed upbeat of the theme, an antiphony that is exploited in the development section (especially from b.47 onwards). The movement is irresistibly lively and brilliant. First it should be mastered as an Allegretto, with care over the short-slurred semiquavers in b.14. Then increase the tempo to about ♩=120, at which speed four notes will suffice for the trills in bb.9 and 11. The element of variation is strong and should be enjoyed to the full, e.g. compare bb.24–27 with bb.16–19, and bb.28–29 with bb.32–33. Also with

bb.93–94, where the trills are best played short (as suggested) to ensure a good attack on the succeeding bars. A fraction of extra time, but not as much as a *ritardando*, may be needed to show the subtle harmonic return in b.61, and no one will mind the r.h. taking over the l.h. quaver at the end of b.80 – provided it is done imperceptibly.

D.M.

TEXTUAL NOTES

Composition   Munich, Jan–Feb 1775

Source   autograph (formerly in Preussische Staatsbibliothek, Berlin)

Notes

1st movt
bar

11–12   RH slurring ambiguously placed; reading here by analogy with 29–30

2nd movt
bar

32   1st, 2nd and last time bars not separately notated; fermata on LH $b\natural$ makes clear execution as shown

SONATA in E flat

K282/189g (1775)

© 1971 by The Associated Board of the Royal Schools of Music

A.B. 1515

MENUETTO I

MENUETTO II

Primo Menuetto Da Capo

SONATA in G, K283/189*h*

1 Mozart more than once wrote of his six early sonatas, K279–284, as 'difficult'. Bearing in mind his disdain of empty virtuosity – he was to call Clementi 'a mere *mechanicus*' – he probably referred as much to their stylistic problems (for others) as to their occasional technical hurdles, which are nowhere extreme. K283 is a case in point. It may easily fall a prey to characterless or facile performance and such associations may have led one Mozart authority to describe it as 'otherwise placid', the exception being the fiery finale. But is the first movement so placid? Within ten bars the opening theme grows from tenderness to brilliance, and the dynamic marks reveal, in both senses of the term, Mozart's delight in the *fortepiano* (see bb.5 and 6). In the second group too there is eagerness, if not agitation, in the r.h. syncopations and 'Scotch snaps' (b.23 onwards). Try playing the crotchets *on the* beat, with even quavers in b.25, and compare the resulting 'placidity'. In b.31 a tauter rhythm arises, with the *forte* marks precisely contrasted, and a full tone needs sustaining through bb.34–37. The further trick of jumping, in practice, from b.32 to b.35 will only require trying once to appreciate the harmonic intensity of the 'missing' bb.33–34. Keep up the *forte* in b.43, which makes playful counterpoint out of the earlier starker transition, and make the *piano* in b.45 sudden, as it unexpectedly recalls bb.23–24. Another subtlety is the hemiola effect at the resumption of the *forte* – two-four sequences cutting across the three-four time – which ties up neatly with the l.h. chords in bb.8–9. Even the conventional repeated cadence has a touch of the mature Mozart in its C♮–C♯ interplay.

The nature and scale of the material do not call for extended development, and bb.54–62 agreeably mark time with a new character and its own variant. From b.62 the return is already in sight. When it comes (end of b.72) the first subject is twice humorously interrupted, suggesting that overflow of the spirit of development again typical of the later Mozart. The tempo is that of a lively but still graceful minuet, and in fact the minuets of K282 (and of Beethoven's Op.49 no.2) are useful guides. The one technical hurdle, bb.30 and 97, concerns the awkward l.h. leap on the third beat. Some editions suggest a r.h. takeover and another alternative is simply to hand over the final note of the previous group. A slight hiatus may add to the humour of the sudden *forte*, but its screening spontaneity will demand careful practice.

2 Although the marking *andante* should warn against heaviness, the repeated quavers at the start may lure the player into a laborious eight-in-a-bar effect. One help is to think of the opening as a variant of the Schubertian rhythm ♩ ♫ with a basic pulse of crotchets. Another, not to be scorned by pianists, is to practise conducting such a movement in silence as a means of sensing the music's natural flow – a method advocated by Heinrich Neuhaus, the teacher of Gilels and Richter. This too will reveal the amount of surface variety from one phrase to the next, e.g. the sharp but lightly-touched dotted rhythm of bb.5 and 6 that moves into smooth semiquavers in bb.7 and 8. The dynamics should not be exaggerated; they are like the vocal inflections of a monologue with no place for violent antiphony. The movement is in sonata-form with a miniature development that rescues itself from a too soon return to C major in b.18. Notice the rare contrapuntal interplay at this point.

3 The chain of events up to b.40 constitutes a single theme constantly expanding and extending itself through its own irrepressible energy. Yet the energy is light-footed even in the brilliant *forte* eruptions. A quick one-in-a-bar should still take note of the vital rests in b.2 etc.: this feature is important in the l.h. of bb.19–24 where it contrasts with the held-through r.h. suspensions. The theme capriciously reverts to its original topic from b.33 onwards. After the smoothness of bb.41–56 the repartee between the hands returns, a challenge to their equality of execution. The syncopated figure in b.65, etc., marks the arrival of a rebellious character but bb.71–73 restore it to order. In the development the dramatic outbursts in bb.107 and 115 are most eloquent if the *forte* is maintained evenly throughout the r.h. semiquavers with no undue accents on the bar-lines.

D.M.

TEXTUAL NOTES

Composition   Munich, Jan–Feb 1775

Source   autograph (formerly in Preussische Staatsbibliothek, Berlin)

Notes

1st movt
bar

57	RH slur may begin on $f''\sharp$
107	Mozart misplaced the LH treble clef, giving *1* as $F\sharp$

3rd movt
bar

35,37	our notation follows Mozart's, perhaps suggesting accent on first note (also 206, 208)
43–4, 49–50	original (except RH, 50) has bars slurred singly cf. 41–2, 214–15, 220–3
99–100	Mozart originally wrote all notes stacc., then changed to slurs

SONATA in G

K283/189h (1774-5)

© 1976 by The Associated Board of the Royal Schools of Music

A.B.1604

Andante

74

A.B.1604

Presto

81

A.B.1604

SONATA in D, K284/205*b*

On 17 October 1777 Mozart wrote from Augsburg to his father about Stein's fortepianos. 'Here and at Munich I have played all my six sonatas by heart several times,' he added, mentioning that the last of them, the D major, sounded 'exquisite' on Stein's instrument. These six works are K279–284, though the revised Köchel numbers (K189*d–h* and K205*b*) date them two or three years earlier than the tour in question. The D major, while fulfilling the key-scheme of the set, was composed especially for Baron von Dürnitz at Munich in 1775. Although the Baron never paid for the commission, the sonata proved its value for Mozart as a display piece and was the only one of the six to be published in his lifetime. In many ways it was the most ambitious of the earlier sonatas, abounding in dynamic contrasts and orchestral effects; observation of these is a first requirement for the player. Such passages as those from b.13 and b.38 in the first movement have the clear ring of orchestral tuttis. The other movements are formal departures, supposedly influenced by the 'French' manner – at Dürnitz's request? – and the extensive variations of the finale call for the finest control of character and texture if they are not to outstay their welcome.

1　It should go without saying that the somewhat proud nature of the opening depends on precision of note-values and rests, with equal stress and separation for the three crotchets in b.2. The phrases from b.4 and b.9 introduce the sudden contrasts of *p* and *f*. Thinking in terms of strings reinforced by wind-players from time to time will prevent unmusical abruptness and alert the pianist's orchestral sense. The continuous *f* passages, b.7 and b.13, will then be carried through more resolutely. From b.22 the second-group theme, *cantabile* in feeling, takes the dominant key into its own hands with the lightest l.h. accompaniment. The *f* in b.30 is again *subito*, and special care over fingering is needed to reveal the harmonic subtlety from b.34 onwards. Emphasize the rhythmic difference between b.44 and b.50, the former relating back to b.40, even to b.10.

The development is technically and musically exacting since the l.h. crossings may tend to break up the music into one-bar phrases and disrupt the semiquaver flow beneath. Note that the harmony moves in *two*-bar periods. The *f* in b.60 is dramatic, suggesting that the whole section from b.52 may be taken, by contrast, gently rather than vigorously. In any case the emotional implications of minor-key tonality prevail until the sudden release in b.70. Although the recapitulation appears 'regular' at first glance, the imaginative changes of octave in the second group should be noted, bb.93–96 and bb.106–108 being answered by their variants in a higher register. The extra climb in b.97 brings a delightful extension of phrase-length. A further innovation is the passage from b.118 to b.121, serving the purpose of a coda within a codetta.

2　In the previous Associated Board edition Aubyn Raymar warned hearers not to expect the characteristic rhythm and vigour associated with Chopin's polonaises. The 3/4 time, the feminine cadences (b.8, b.16) and occasional syncopations (bb.21–24, b.45) are all however gently typical of the original folk-dance. The rondo element, with returns at b.31 and b.70, is enhanced by variations which are a guide to the basic tempo. There is also a vocal quality in the theme which reflects Mozart's operas of the time, *La finta giardiniera* and *Il rè pastore* (in which Aminta's aria 'L'amerò' begins with an identical phrase). The figure in b.2 becomes an accompanying feature of the movement and should be phrased and shaded as marked. It is worth differentiating between the solitary trill and the other ornaments in episode one (b.19) since this whole procedure is repeated in the second episode. The surprise move from relative minor to subdominant in the latter case (b.53) became a favoured device in Mozart's mature sonata-rondos and the resultant mood-change should be made clear. So should the magic effect of the twice-interrupted cadence in bb.85 and 87, delaying fulfilment until after the pause-bar.

3　It is vital to strike a tempo that allows the theme and the first six variations to unfold without hiatus or noticeable change of gear. Therefore read the *andante* of the first edition as 'at a walking pace' rather than 'slowish', taking only the slightest breath between one variation and the next. Otherwise the gavotte-like upbeat will lose its point. A leisurely two-in-a-bar will provide the momentum. The varied slurrings in the theme, ironed out in many editions, add to its character if touched in lightly: they may be taken to indicate local stresses, and the difference between b.7 and b.16 is worth observing. The timing of the rests in bb.12–13 is of course important since this extra bar is treated wittily later. Once the pulse is established the jostling of triplets and semiquavers in Var.2 should be no problem, with Var.3 following naturally in its wake.

A longer breath before the *minore* variation is recommended, but any expressive stretching of the tempo should be countered by the prompt and precise handling of Vars.8–10. Var.11, a real *adagio*, will need to be more than twice as slow if the elaborations in b.198, b.200, etc., are to be taken in a consistent tempo – coloratura maybe, but still *cantabile*! – without losing sense of the original harmonic framework. Although most players will prefer to take the published version, a comparison with the autograph (as with the slow movement of K332) throws much light on Mozart's practice. After this, in Var.12, the *allegro* three-four is best taken steadily to ensure clarity and vitality in the l.h. semiquavers and to leave room for the *pp* at b.250.

D.M.

TEXTUAL NOTES

Composition   Munich, Feb–March 1775

Sources   autograph (formerly in Preussische Staatsbibliothek, Berlin) [A]; first edition, as no.2 of *Trois sonates pour le clavecin ou pianoforte . . . composèes par Mr W. A. Mozart, dedièes a son excellence Madame la Comtesse Terese de Kobenzl . . . Oeuvre VII* (Vienna: Christoph Torricella, 1784) [E] (the other sonatas in the publication are K333/315c and the violin sonata K454).

Notes   Text normally follows A; significant discrepancies in E are noted, as are points where E text is preferred. E lacks all arpeggiation marks.

1st movt
bar

5	A, RH crotchet may be stacc., more likely a smudge; omitted, particularly as lacking at analogous points
7–8	E, sqs slurred in 4s (also 13, 25–6, 79; not 78, 96–8)
16,87	A, RH lower part, 2nd half of bar, dsqs instead of sqs
17,19	E, *a″* stacc. lacking
22,93	slurring from E; A has 22 slurred in one, 93 in pairs
23,94	E, 2nd *tr* lacking
26	dynamics from E
27,98	A, length of 2nd slur ambiguous; possibly (especially in 98) it should not extend to *4*; E, ties from last note lacking
28	slur from E
29	1st slur from E
40,43	E, LH lacks lower octave (though present 112, 115); slurs from E
51	A, *e″* lacking in 2nd chord
56	A, *g″* written as crotchet
97–8	dynamics from E
112,115	E, slur covers last 3 beats; cf. 40, 43
119	*f*, RH and LH, from E
121	A, 1st chord, lowest note wrongly *É*
122–3	slurs from E

2nd movt
bar

1	E has *sf*, also in 3, 5–6, 13–14, 29, 65, where A has *f*
5	E, LH 2nd chord, middle note *e′* (cf. 43, where A and E each have *d′*); LH slur from E
7–8	LH cresc., *p*, slur and RH 1st slur in 8 from E
9,11	E, RH lacks slur
17	A, 1st ornament ambiguous; E has *tr* for each ornament in 17–20, 53–6
17–19	E, LH slurred in 4s (also 53–4)
19	LH *7*, perhaps ✕; also 55, ♯
29	LH slur from E
32	slurs from E (also LH, 34)
37	E, RH 1st beat ♫♫; *cresc.* from E
38	lower octaves in LH and dynamics from E; A has slur, *a–c♯*
43–4	E, RH last beat ♪ ⁷ ♪
55	stacc. (accent) from E
63	E, RH *1* stacc., *2–4* slurred
65	A, RH *9–12* in 1 slur; E as shown
74	A, slur across 1st 2 beats; stacc. from E (also 75)
85,87	E, no *f* on 1st beat, but *sf* on 2nd

3rd movt   Tempo marks at head of movt and for Var. 12 from E

bar

12	slurs and *fp* marks from E
17	A, RH triplets slurred in 3s; E as shown
20–33	20, 27 (beats 1–4) and 24, 33 (beats 2–4): A, RH slurred in 3s; E as shown
Var.2	LH slurring in 6s all from E
46	last slurs, RH and LH, from E
56	E, RH slurred *1–8, 9–12, 13–16*
57	stacc. from E
59–60	A, RH slurred in 8s; E as shown
65	E, RH slurred in 4s
66	A gives *p*, E *pp*
67	A, RH slurred *1–4, 5–16*; E as shown
Var. 4	A, LH, 69–70 slurred in 8s; 71, 75, 84 all in 4s: E reading preferred
70	RH slur from E
79	E, *tr* lacking
85–92	dynamics from E
102–3, 114–16	stacc. from E
109	A, last 3 notes *d′–e′–d′*
125	A, RH *3 c″♯*, with illegible correction; E as shown
126	slur from E
131–5	all dynamics except final *p* (RH and LH) from E; A has *f*, 132, RH, and 133, LH
135	A lacks ♯ to *g″*
136–9	stacc. (except 2nd half 138) from E
150–1	RH slurs from E
153	crotchet *a′* stacc., A and E: ?error, as none at analogous points, except E, LH, 157
Var.9	stacc. from E: RH, 157–9, 162, 165–8; LH, 157, 166–8
160,169	slurs from E
162	A, RH *3–4*, not *4–5*, slurred
164	A, Mozart apparently deleted slur between last 2 notes (though it is in E), replacing by stacc. on *f′♯*
171–2	LH slurs from E
174	RH *f* from E
181–2	A has *p* at start of 181, *pp* in 182; E reading, with *decrescendo*, *p* and RH *f* as shown, preferred
Var.11	A text shown in small type, E in normal; in A, Mozart wrote out 1st version of each strain (187–95, 203–12), then added the varied repeats, indicating their insertion
199	A, ornament ambiguous
206	E, LH *ſ e′*
217	E, *d′* lacking in grace-note group
219	E, last quaver ♪♫♫♫
221	E, 1st chord, *a′* for *g′*
222,243	E, 1st 2 notes shown as qs
221–6	dynamics from E
224	RH slur from E
229–30	A gives RH *f* only in 230 (similarly 246–7); E gives it in 229 as shown
246	A, LH lacks *f♯*

83

SONATA in D

K 284/205*b* (1775)

© 1978 by The Associated Board of the Royal Schools of Music

A.B.1672

86

A.B.1672

88

RONDEAU EN POLONAISE
Andante

* R H *g'♯* to coincide with LH *d'*, *b'* with *b* ; similarly in bar 81.

THEMA
Andante

Var. 4

Var. 7
Minore

Var. 8
Maggiore

Var. 10

Var. 11*
Adagio cantabile

* A—revised in first edition; B—version in Mozart's autograph (see Textual Notes).

A.B.1672

SONATA in C, K309/284*b*

Mozart and his mother arrived in Mannheim on 30 October 1777. After only five days he wrote to his father mentioning a sonata for Rosa Cannabich (K309) which was 'almost finished save for the Rondo'. Yet before leaving Augsburg he had referred – in a letter of 23 October – to a sonata in C major which he had played there 'all of a sudden' out of his head. Whether the Mannheim work drew upon its material is not clear. Whatever the true facts, the Andante of K309 was apparently composed specifically for Rosa and she was to play it 'with the utmost expression'. Her playing of the whole gave Mozart 'indescribable pleasure', and such praise was not lightly won. From Augsburg he had written of a still younger prodigy, daughter of the piano-maker Stein, whose instruments Mozart so much admired: 'She will never acquire the most essential, the most difficult and chief requisite in music, which is, time . . .'. Of his own playing Mozart added that 'everyone is amazed that I can always keep strict time', a remark that need not be interpreted metronomically but should be taken to heart by all Mozart players. In the same letter he made his famous remark about passages 'which ought to flow like oil'. Mlle Rosa's playing presumably fulfilled these demands.

1 The tempo of the movement is gauged by the feeling that the opening minims hold two live crotchets within them, each capable of further subdivision. Doubts about keeping 'strict time' can be settled by studying this opening figure in the context of its last appearance, bb.152–153, where it is surrounded by semiquavers that should 'flow like oil'. The theme itself, soon to be adopted and adapted in the minuet of K331 in A, has its importance underlined by the octave doubling: it should not be regarded as a cliché. For the *piano* reply, expect a matching two bars but receive, or give, five. This subtlety of phrase-length is reflected in the three-bar phrases from b.15, where the initial repeated-note figure may be thought of as a variant of the original answer.

From b.21, the transition theme, the *fp* effects are orchestral. The Mannheim orchestra was renowned for such effects, and in the world of the keyboard Mozart found good fortepianos in Mannheim as well as Augsburg. The modern pianist, used to instant dynamics, should not lose the drama of precision. In bb.27–32 the *forte* is kept up, with exact l.h. crotchets and no suspicion of triplets underlying the dotted rhythm of b.31. The following lead-in, bb.33–34, was recalled at the same point in the later C major Sonata, K545. Here in K309 the l.h. legato offsets the sharper articulation of the r.h. – an effect reversed in bb.127–132. Show the slight difference between bb.37–38 and 41–42 by listening to the rests. In b.42 the last three l.h. quavers are *f subito*, setting the character of the succeeding passage. Bar 45 contains an amusing diminution of bb.35–36, an effect that is *not* repeated three bars later, where the mood harks back. In these largely diatonic surroundings, the diminished-7th harmony in b.50 is an 'event' not to be taken lightly. After the cadential trill, bb.54–58 are an unexpected extension, with the *forte* a variant of the *piano* phrase: note the r.h. changes of octave, which are brought into line in the recapitulation (bb.150–151).

The development is more than usually concerned with the first subject, with echo-effects indicated by the marks (bb.62, 89). A turn to minor keys, including the impassioned outburst at b.73, leaves an imprint on the recapitulation too: the spirit of development persists in bb.101–108, as it does in many of Mozart's later sonata-form movements. Elsewhere there are changes beyond the demands of form, key or compass: the double-counterpoint effect from b.127 is one, the extra leap in b.141 another.

2 'Moreover, she likes playing it', wrote Mozart about Mlle Rosa and her own character-study. As she was 'very intelligent and steady for her age', other intelligent players will take a broad view of the movement, noting every new feature as it arises. Mozart's request 'not too quickly' is indicated by *un poco adagio* and demanded by the music itself, which gathers variants continually. It may be regarded as a set of variations with an extra 12-bar episode from b.33 that is itself varied from b.53. In the theme itself, bb.1–8, note-values are as subtle as the changes of stress from second beat to first (b.5). For example, the rising semiquavers in b.4 are answered in b.5 by slurred pairs descending, and both contrast with the previous dotted rhythm. Remember Mozart's other words about 'strict time', trying out bb.1, 17, 25, 45 and 65 in succession: the basic tempo does not change with the elaboration. Note the change of register in b.30, and play the long phrasing from bb.40 and 60 with the finest legato possible.

3 The warning about tempo applies equally to Mozart's Allegretto finales, which are often played too fast – note the word *grazioso*. The pulse should be steady enough to encompass triplet movement (b.40) and demisemiquavers (b.58, etc.). These last are humorously orchestral – in deference to, or in preparation for, Mannheim? This rondo makes a point of dynamic contrasts, right up to the closing bars, where control of the markings should produce a natural fading-away.

If the opening sounds like an oboe and clarinet duet, so much the better. The childlike manner is but a starting-point and the C♯ bass in b.13 can be enjoyed without emphasis. An extension of compass in bb.16–17 is a foretaste of brilliance to come. As with the first movement, minor-key inflections gather later. Observe the sudden *p* in bb.43 and 53: these devices are as much expressive as resourceful, and throw into relief the comparative unconcern of the F major episode (b.116). With Mozart, more than any other composer, simplicities run deep – or so the player should believe. Although Leopold Mozart spoke of the 'mannered Mannheim style' he admitted that there was not enough of it to spoil Mozart's 'own good style'.

D.M.

TEXTUAL NOTES

Composition Mannheim, Oct–Nov 1777

Sources autograph lost; an MS copy by Leopold Mozart (to whom Mozart sent his own MS shortly after the sonata's composition) survives in a Swiss private collection and a photocopy has kindly been made available by the Neue Mozart-Ausgabe [L]; the first edition is as no.1 of *Trois sonates pour le clavecin ou le forte piano* (Paris: Heina, 1782) (nos.2 and 3 are K310/300*d* and K311/284*c*) [E]; and two copies in Stift Melk, Austria, have also been consulted, by kind permission of the librarian, the earlier being no.1 in a set 'Sechs Sonaten' [M1], the later 'Sonata in C per il clavi cembalo o forte piano' [M2]

Notes M1 has much additional slurring, not shown here, and some additional dynamic marks, some of which are included here editorially where justified by analogy with L or E

1st movt E gives tempo as 'Allegro con spiritoso'
bar

13–14	L, slurs possibly *1–4*
15–19, 110–14	alternate *p* and *f* not in L; in E only 113–14; M1 has as shown in 15–19 except *p* in 16 (that and *p-f-p* in 110–11 editorial by analogy with 113–14)
21–6, 116–22	M1 gives *fp* on 1st note of each 2-bar phrase, *cresc.* later in bar (not 23)
23,25	arpeggiation from E
24	stacc. from E.
27	M1, *f* on *1*, *sf* on *c'''* (also 28)
33–4	LH dynamics not in E
38,41	RH, 3rd slur from E
42	LH *f* in M1 only, though implied by stacc. wedges in L; RH slurs from E
43	*f* from E
48–9, 142–3	dynamics reversed in E
58	arpeggiation from E
63	*p* from E
74–8	slurs not in E
80–1	stacc. from E, 80, final note, 81, *1–4*
89	E has *p* for *pp*
91	slurs from E
98	LH, 2nd slur from E
103	E, RH *6♮* for ♭; *p* from E
106	L, LH ♮ for ♭ to *a*
112	L, LH *3 d*
120	arpeggiation from E
124	M1, LH, crotchet *g–g'* 1st beat, q rest, then as other sources
128	*f* not in E
129	LH *p* not in E
131	LH, 3rd slur from E
136	LH *f* as 42

2nd movt E slurring less careful and less complete than L; divergences in E not detailed unless they supply a deficiency in L or might represent valid alternative readings
bar

6	L no slur 1st beat; E, slur *1–3*: cf. 5, 49
8	L slur *1–3*, none in E; L, RH *e'* missing
10	L, LH 2nd *c'* missing
13	L slur ?*2–4*
17–18	L has only *f*; E has *fp* (RH), *f* (LH) in 17, *fp* (LH) in 18

22	*f* in E
27	LH 2nd slur from E
30–1	E, RH slurs over dsqs
32	LH slur and tie from E
33	RH 2nd slur from E
36	RH slur from E
38	E, RH last note *b''♭* (a possible reading)
54	RH 2nd slur from E
61	*f''* not ♯ in L (but ♮ in 62 implies accidental omission)
63	L, *g'* marked ♯ in error; last 2 slurs from E
65	RH last slur from E
67	E (also M1 and M2), *d'* for *f'*
73	L, LH slur *1–3*; none in E
76	RH 1st slur from E
77	*pp* from E
78	E, RH *e* lacking

3rd movt E: 'Rondau   Allegretto gratioso'
bar

1	*p* from E; LH slurring in 4s (also 93ff, 116ff) by analogy with L, 189–93 and E, 189, 194; RH slurs by analogy with E, 93–8
1,3,11	stacc. by analogy with L, 95, 195; also 93, 99, 189, 191
19	*f* from E
32	L, RH articulation lacking in 2nd half of bar
42	slur from E
43	*f* from E
54	L, LH last *f'♯* lacking
66	*p* from E
68	slur from E
71	some edns give LH 1st chord *g–b♭*, but L and E agree *b♮*; the same applies to 175 (*e♭/♮*) and 226 (*f♮/♯*)
76	L, 2nd chord, *d''* lacking
77–82	sources ambiguous about dot/wedge stacc.; also 210–18
85	E, LH last 3 qs slurred; *f* from E
93ff	see 1
108–9	E has RH only *3* and *4* stacc., slurs *5–8*
110	E has RH slurs *5–6*, *7–8*, last one lacking in LH
115	E, RH *2 b''♭*
117,121	LH altered in later edns to give dominant harmony on 1st beat; text here as in L and E
119	LH, L has ♭ to *3* and *6*, and *7* is *a'*; E has ♮ to *3*, ♭ to *6*, and *7* is *g'*
124, 127–8	LH altered in later edns, 1st beat of 124 and 128, last of 127; text here as in L and E
127	2nd slur from E
132–6	articulation from E in 133; E lacks slurs 132, 134, 136
162	L 1st chord *c–c'*; *e–c'*, as in E, clearly correct
167	L, top note of LH chord *c*; E gives *d*; cf. 67
189ff	see 1
201	L, *c'''* for *e'''*
217–18	no stacc. in E
226	see 71
228	*p* from E
230–1	RH top note *e'''* in L, E and M2 (with no ♮ in 232 to suggest an omission); M1 and some later edns give the harmonically more probable *e'''♭*
236	L, LH *E* and *C* lacking
240	L, LH last chord *g–b–d'*; text follows E and analogy with 241
245ff	E, LH articulation lacking

SONATA in C

K309/284b (1777)

Allegro con spirito

* The alternate *f-p* here and in bars 110-11 should be regarded as optional: see Textual Notes.

© 1973 by The Associated Board of the Royal Schools of Music

A.B.1560

Andante un poco adagio

RONDEAU
Allegretto grazioso

130

133

* see Textual Notes

A.B.1560

SONATA in A minor, K310/300d

The A minor Sonata is a landmark in Mozart's earlier keyboard works, only paralleled in pathos and intensity by the later Fantasy and Sonata in C minor. This turning to the minor key has been related by some writers, including Alfred Einstein, to the turbulent emotions in Mozart's personal life: his affair with Aloysia Weber and reluctant departure from Mannheim; the death of his mother in Paris; and his bitterness at the vicissitudes of the freelance musician in search of success and security. It may be wishful thinking to view the Sonata as a direct outcome of such experiences, since Mozart always composed from the fullness of his more generalized knowledge of human feelings. Other influences should be borne in mind by the interpreter, among them the *Sturm und Drang* movement which swept through the arts during the 1770s. The eloquence of Haydn's minor-key works of that time was not lost on the young Mozart. His own early G minor Symphony K183 and E minor Violin and Piano Sonata K304 showed his instinctive grasp of the emotional implications offered by a minor-key recapitulation in sonata form. This subtle resource also enhanced the profound slow movements of his two greatest earlier concertos, the Eb Piano Concerto K271 and the Sinfonia Concertante for Violin and Viola. All these works are worth studying in connection with the present Sonata which, whatever impulse may have prompted it, should be approached as a tragic masterpiece from the first bar.

1   The word *maestoso*, literally 'majestic', is, however, a warning against impetuosity, and a tempo of ♩=112–120 should suffice to give forward movement to the drama as well as grandeur. No note should go to waste in the repeated l.h. chords, which can too easily undermine the dignity of the r.h. theme. It is helpful to emulate the balance and texture of a string quartet, avoiding the tyranny of the bar-line by thinking forward to each change of harmony. Arguments persist about the length of the appoggiatura in the second bar, since Mozart's notation seems consistently inconsistent: compare b.2 with b.10, and b.51 with b.89 (l.h.). It is unlikely that he intended such a salient melodic feature to fluctuate, but there is room for doubt. On the other hand the short grace-note suggested for b.1 should not be crushed: the D♯ is both fully melodic and dramatically dissonant. The precision of note-values and rests is vital in bb.6 and 7 where the operatic crotchet-quaver slurs require little or no pedal. From b.16 a more orchestral manner takes over, with an authentic echo effect in the Mannheim style.

The 'second group', from the end of b.22 to the close of the exposition, is remarkably unified in its continuous semiquavers which should follow Mozart's precept and 'flow like oil'. A slight increase in tempo may assist the flow, but it should be held firmly in check when the dotted rhythm returns at b.45. The passage-work is in fact more melodic than brilliant, and the changing nature of the l.h. contribution keeps the texture alive, e.g. the rich two-part writing and suspensions in bb.28–32. In the development, having released the tension by giving the first subject in the relative major, Mozart launches into the strenuous passage of sequences from b.58, in which the extreme contrasts of *ff* and *pp* are most dramatic

when taken *subito*. Slow practice should ensure that the r.h. dotted rhythm coincides with the l.h. semiquavers, and the energy of the whole section depends as much on the semitonal clashes in the bass as on the clear contrapuntal playing in the r.h. The effect will be spoilt if the deep bass-notes are prolonged with pedal. In b.80 the D♯ grace-note is omitted as being awkwardly redundant after the chromatic lead-in – see Dr Sadie's textual notes.

From b.104 the changed features of the material in its minor-key transformation intensify the drama: the undulating l.h. figure, the Neapolitan harmony in b.119, and the diminished-seventh irruptions in bb.126–127. The final chords may be closely but crisply spread to match those in b.49.

2   This expressive movement is enriched by the wealth of dynamic marks that Mozart lavished on it, though in general *f* and *fp* are best regarded as melodic stresses and not dramatic interventions – except in the passage from b.43, which introduces a more sternly rhythmic and dissonant element. The test of a player's *cantabile* comes at the start, with the F major arpeggio leading to and away from the high A like a single voice. The richness of the melodic line depends, as so often, on the subtlety of the l.h. support and the note-values need careful watching, e.g. the quavers in bb.4 and 7. In the transition theme, b.12 may require stretching a little to take in its profusion of ornament, but the basic pulse, befitting an *andante*, is a leisurely three-in-a-bar rather than six. The lead-in to the second group at the end of b.14 is taken *f* and with resolution, like an assertive cellist in a quartet. From b.15 the new theme requires delicate handling with a light separation of the l.h. quavers. Compare the slow movement of the 'Haffner' Symphony, second subject, for a clue to the texture. As hinted before, the *fp* markings from b.19 and particularly from b.22 are wholly melodic and not to be overdone. Those in the development, bb.38 and 40, are more overtly dramatic, preparing for the climactic passage that follows, reflecting the first movement's development at the same point. The *pp* in b.52 and the new harmonic move at b.62 will gain in eloquence by being taken in a spirit of improvisation.

3   The short slurs in the r.h. and the quaver rests in the l.h. give this movement an obsessive and haunted quality not unlike the finale of Beethoven's D minor Sonata Op.31 no.2. Both end in an unrelenting minor, though Beethoven's is marked *allegretto* and Mozart's *presto*. The tempo is obviously urgent but should not preclude one from imagining a split-second's breath between the slurs, which are never to be phrased across the bar-line. The quavers are to be taken lightly on the release of the dotted crotchets, but not at the expense of the longer line of the music. Another feature of the movement is its proneness to explosive dynamics, but note the difference between the sudden *f* in bb.17–20 and the quick *crescendo* in bb.26–28. The suggested fingering from b.37 may seem awkward but clarifies the phrasing: the l.h. alternative of *5213* is worth trying but risks a hiatus within as well as between the bars. Observe the unexpected three-bar phrase in bb.49–51 and be sparing with the pedal from b.64, where

the l.h. octaves emulate the r.h. slurs in the rondo-theme.

The form is a sonata-rondo with a monothematic absorption in its opening figure. In the middle episode, b.143, a musette-like idea provides a temporary haven in A major, best played close to the keys and with lightness and simplicity but yielding just a touch of pathos with the minor-key inflections in bb.161–165. The leads into b.143 and b.175 need no *ritardando* beyond a slight 'placing' to mark the surprise of the major and the return of the minor. The closing section increases in intensity, and the shock of bb.199–202 is carried through in sustained *f*. A keen orchestral sense is called for in the last three lines. Reducing the 'scoring' to a pair of oboes in bb.233–236 will underline the abrupt contrast of dynamics. This passage may be divided between the hands, in which case the r.h. fingering should replace *5454*, etc., with *4343*. Short slurs may be implied here in the manner of the rondo-theme. Note that the canon in bb.245–250 includes the repeated octave Es, and treat the final chords with orchestral precision.

D.M.

TEXTUAL NOTES

Composition Paris, summer 1778

Sources autograph, in New York private collection (formerly in the Preussische Staatsbibliothek, Berlin) [A]; first edition, as no.2 of *Trois sonates pour le clavecin ou le forte piano . . . Oeuvre IV* (Paris: Heina, 1782) [E]

Notes The text basically follows A; where E is the source of an emendation or a possible alternative reading this is noted below, but faults in E, which is inaccurate, are noted only when of possible significance

1st movt
A: LH notated in tenor clef, 1–5 (1st beat), 9–14 (1st beat); in alto clef, 50–6, 104–5

bar
3   A lacks slur
6   E has *f* (no *p* in LH, or *f* in 9)
7   staccato marks in E
9   as 3
10   LH top note *e'* in E (also originally in A, but altered)
22   LH bottom note *B'* in E
45   *f* editorial: Mozart gave no dynamic marks in A after 23 but it is inconceivable that *forte* should not be reached by this point, if not sooner; E gives *f* at 49
46   E has *f* in middle of bar, but this is a misreading of Mozart's clarifying instruction 'si' next to the smudged note *b'* in A
50–6 LH all 8ve lower in E as in all passages which in A are in alto clef in this sonata (except 104–5 in this movement, 167–74 in 3rd movement); this seems certain to be an error

76–7 notated as 'bis' from 74–5; presumably LH *E–e* chord not intended in 76 (though thus in E)
80–7 not written out; Mozart's instruction 'Da capo 8 mesures'; *d♯″* acciaccatura omitted as clearly redundant (though thus in E)
92   RH, 2nd half of bar, lower note *e'* in A, *f'* (correctly) in E; LH, last slur in E only
111   LH, last beat, A♯ *g–b♯*, E♯ *g–d'♯*
126   *f* editorial; cf. 45 above; E gives *f* at 133

2nd movt
A: LH notated in alto clef, 6 (3rd crotchet)–7, 15 (2nd)–19 (1st), 28 (3rd)–30 (1st), 36 (2nd and 3rd), 66 (3rd)–67 (1st, 1st note of 2nd), 70 (2nd note)–72 (1st note): all these passages notated an 8ve lower in E

bar
4   Mozart's slurring ambiguous; it seems to read:

5   RH hard to decipher, probably on 2nd and 3rd crotchets; any correction involves guesswork (ours preserves the 2nd repeated *c″*, which also appears in E: 1st time, as A in 59)

20   RH stacc. only in E
27   *p* here exactly as placed by Mozart; possibly it should be at *9* or *17*
44–9 A, original notation: etc
54–60 not written out; Mozart's instruction 'Da capo 7 mesures'
81   A: RH *p* halfway through bar; but cf. 26
82   analogous to 27

3rd movt
bar
1–20 LH slurring left exactly as Mozart wrote it, despite apparent inconsistency, as its presence or absence has definite harmonic significance (also 107–21, 175–93)
8   possibly LH chord *e–e'* intended on 1st beat, but it seems that Mozart originally wrote, then eliminated, the *e* (which is retained in E)
91–4 LH, 1 slur per bar (except 92), but cf. 87–90
107   see 1–20
159–60 RH, 1 slur per bar (at end/beginning of staff)
167   LH in alto clef to 174, *1*
173   RH upper notes *b'*, *c″*, *d″* (crotchet, 2 qs) in A; E as shown
175   see 1–20
226–9 RH slurred only 227, 229, 1 slur per bar; cf. LH and 56–9

SONATA in A minor

K310/300*d* (1778)

Allegro maestoso

© 1981 by The Associated Board of the Royal Schools of Music

A.B. 1691

Andante cantabile

* The rhythmic pattern shown for bar 20 may be preferred here and in parallel contexts (e.g. bars 24, 25).

154

SONATA in D, K311/284c

The original Köchel numbers are misleading here, as the three piano sonatas K309–11 cannot be considered as a group. K310, the remarkable A minor Sonata, was written in Paris in 1778; K309 and K311 were composed, or at least completed, at Mannheim in November or December of the previous year. In fact the D major, K311, may have been begun in Munich that autumn, and it is probably the sonata Mozart referred to as 'still not ready' in a letter to his cousin on 3 December 1777. His travels that winter brought two important influences on his keyboard writing, one direct, one indirect. In Augsburg, *en route* for Mannheim, he played on Stein's improved fortepianos; and in Mannheim he heard one of the finest orchestras in Europe. His next symphony, the 'Paris', was consciously brilliant, and it was in D major, a resonant open-string key for the orchestra. Such key-associations affect other mediums too. His earlier D major Sonata, the so-called 'Dürnitz' Sonata K284, began with a resolute, crisp, 'orchestral' theme, and its first movement has other points in common with the present work, K311 – the lead into, and the start of, the second group, for example.

1 The opening of K311 not only calls for a keen sense of orchestral colour, a tutti chord followed by oboes and horns, but shows the influence of the concerto form too. The events in bb.1–16 closely resemble those in the first movement of the Eb Piano Concerto, K271 – the astonishingly mature 'early' Eb, written in Salzburg in January 1777, in which the soloist makes a prompt riposte to the orchestra's very first phrase. There is something of this spirited antiphony in K311, whether one regards the first beat of b.4 as an ending or, as in the concerto, an overlap. In the latter case, it is the left hand, not the right, that marks the re-entry of the tutti. Contrast in character should not, however, forestall the first real *piano* in b.7, but the subsequent alternations of *piano* and *forte* continue to suggest the concertante element. Note that the right hand takes the initiative in bb.11, 24, and 66: the left-hand *fortes* come later, a point omitted in some editions, though not of course at the end of b.86, where the major key is triumphantly restored after the unexpected turn to D minor. Although not indicated, the right hand should cross over for the quaver figure in b.27 (compare b.90). Avoid the common fault of attacking the second crotchet of b.30 and elsewhere with a sudden accent: it is the whole phrase that is *forte*, and it should match the previous *piano* one. This feature is delightfully reversed in bb.58–65. Other points to notice are the development's concern with, and sudden abandonment of, the sighing cadence-figure of bb.38–39; and the bypassing of the first subject in the recapitulation. It reappears at b.99, and it may have been the lengthy D major-ness of this section that led Mozart to substitute an interrupted cadence for the expected full close in b.110. The mark 'con spirito' implies a lively crotchet pulse, perhaps a shade livelier than in the first movement of *Eine kleine Nachtmusik*. Nevertheless the semiquavers in bb.13–14 and from b.66 onwards should be just about manageable by a good coloratura. The left-hand slurs in bb.18 and 80 are inconsistent but harmless.

2 Some commentators have remarked on the unusual phrase-lengths of the opening theme, but the eleven repeated bars are in fact incomplete without the twelfth. The unusual feature here is the overlap in b.8, where the treble G both completes the cadence and forms the upbeat of the 'codetta', as the left-hand figure proves. The movement is an object-lesson in discreet embellishment, for each return of the opening brings some new variant. Bar 25, which recalls the first theme within the world of the second, is a Haydnish move. The expressive sequences from b.29, which seem new, derive from b.3. In b.33 Mozart adds trills, and players who begin on the main note can point to the legato slur and the fact that the upper note has already been sounded; but the upper note will enhance the dissonance. Compare the dissonances in bb.23 and 59. Note the reversed dynamics in bb.33–35, and especially from b.69, where the different register allowed Mozart a sudden change of octave: this is an inspiration, not a makeshift, and out of it the further inspiration of bb.72–73 is born. The deep bass crotchets eight bars from the end must obviously be held with pedal, but many early fortepianos had knee-levers which controlled bass and treble dampers independently; on the modern piano the blurring of the right-hand octaves is tolerable, because short-lived, but the sound must be carefully nursed.

3 A sprightly and fully-developed sonata-rondo in 6/8 time, with plenty of brilliant semiquavers and a written-out cadenza (b.173: more strictly a 'lead-in'), inevitably suggests a concerto finale. In that case this particular movement is a forerunner of a type Mozart had yet to adopt in his later piano concertos (K450, K456, K482, K595) and in the so-called 'hunting' finales of the horn concertos. Aubyn Raymar, in the previous Associated Board edition, called for 'grace and lightness'; but there is a masculine robustness in the tambour effects of b.27 and the wide violinistic leaps of b.56. Pianists will benefit, in this last theme, from listening to a good performance of the finale of Mozart's A major Symphony, K201. The middle episode (b.119) follows a favourite plan of Mozart's in introducing a minor-key theme and turning it aside for a carefree one in the subdominant major (see the rondo of the A major concerto, K488). In the first episode and its later reprise, the different placing of the *piano* in bb.58 and 60 is intentional, adding variety and humour to an otherwise straight repetition.

D.M.

TEXTUAL NOTES

Composition   Mannheim, Nov 1777

Sources   autograph (formerly in Preussische Staatsbibliothek, Berlin) [A]; first edition, as no. 3 of *Trois sonates pour le clavecin ou le forte piano . . . Oeuvre IV* (Paris: Heina, 1782) (nos.1 and 2 are K309/284*b* and K310/300*d*) [E]

Notes   The text basically follows A; where E is the source of an emendation or a possible alternative reading this is noted below, but faults in E, which is inaccurate, are noted only when of possible significance.

1st movt   E: 'Allegro con spiritoso'

bar

19,81	stacc. from E
20	E, RH, *1–3* slurred, *4–7* stacc.
29	E, RH, *1–3* slurred, *4–9* stacc.
33	E, RH, slurs *1–6, 7–8, 9–10*
35	slurs from E
41	E lacks ♮
96	E, RH, slurs *1–4, 7–10*
106	E, RH, slur from *6* to 107, *1*
110	E has *b″* in 2nd chord

2nd movt

bar

7	A, slur originally *3–5*, *3–6* slur heavily written above; E ambiguous
10	E, RH *1 b′*
11	E, RH *5 e′*; L, LH 2nd slur missing
28	A, LH, *1* slur; cf. 64
29–30, 33–4	A, LH slurs across 2 qs: cf. 65ff
39	E, LH *3 g*; also 75
45	A, RH slur possibly only last 3 sqs
56	A, LH slur *5–8*: cf. 20

3rd movt   Many inconsistencies in articulation in A (and the inaccurate E provides no clarification). For example, the slur on the first two notes and at similar passages, and the staccato on the first LH quavers, are added on the basis of only very few appearances. Mozart rarely marked staccato the first quaver of a triplet when prefixed by an acciaccatura, and this seems deliberate enough to justify deletion of his dots in 176, 249 and 251.

bar

16–17	slurs in E cover only first 2 notes of each group (also 102–3, 154–5, 256–7)
23	tie from E
58,60	difference in placing of *p* seems intentional: cf. 223, 225 (also in 64–71, 229–36, but these passages are not written out)
159	E lacks turn; A lacks slur, *5–6*
184	A, RH *6 c′♯*
214	A, RH 2nd dot missing

SONATA in D

Allegro con spirito

K311/284c (1777)

© 1971 by The Associated Board of the Royal Schools of Music

A. B. 1516

160

Andante con espressione

RONDEAU
Allegro

Printed in Great Britain by Caligraving Limited Thetford Norfolk